IS THERE SEX AFTER 40?

FOR HIM

BY TONI GOFFE

I REMEMBER WHEN THE ONLY THING YOU WANTED TO TAKE TO BED WAS <u>ME</u>!

First published in Great Britain by
Pendulum Gallery Press
56 Ackender Road, Alton, Hants GU34 1JS

© TONI GOFFE 1992

IS THERE SEX AFTER 40 FOR HIM?
ISBN 0-948912-19-7

PRINTED 1992

Printed in Britain by Abbeyfield Press Northampton

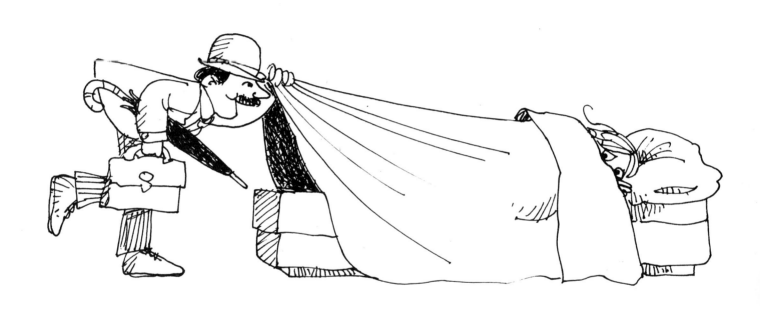

'I SPY, WITH MY LITTLE EYE, SOMETHING BEGINNING WITH.....'

'GEORGE, IT'S ONLY THE FIRST DAY OF THE YEAR THAT YOU'RE GOING TO BE 40! NOW PULL YOURSELF TOGETHER!!'

' CARRY ON DAD, WE'RE JUST HAVING A SEX EDUCATION CLASS FOR OUR TOYS...'

'OH, NO! THEY'RE AT IT AGAIN!!.

'SEE, I TOLD YOU THEY STILL DID IT!' — THAT'S
A POUND YOU OWE ME!'

'I WANT A TRIAL SEPARATION FROM YOU TWO...'

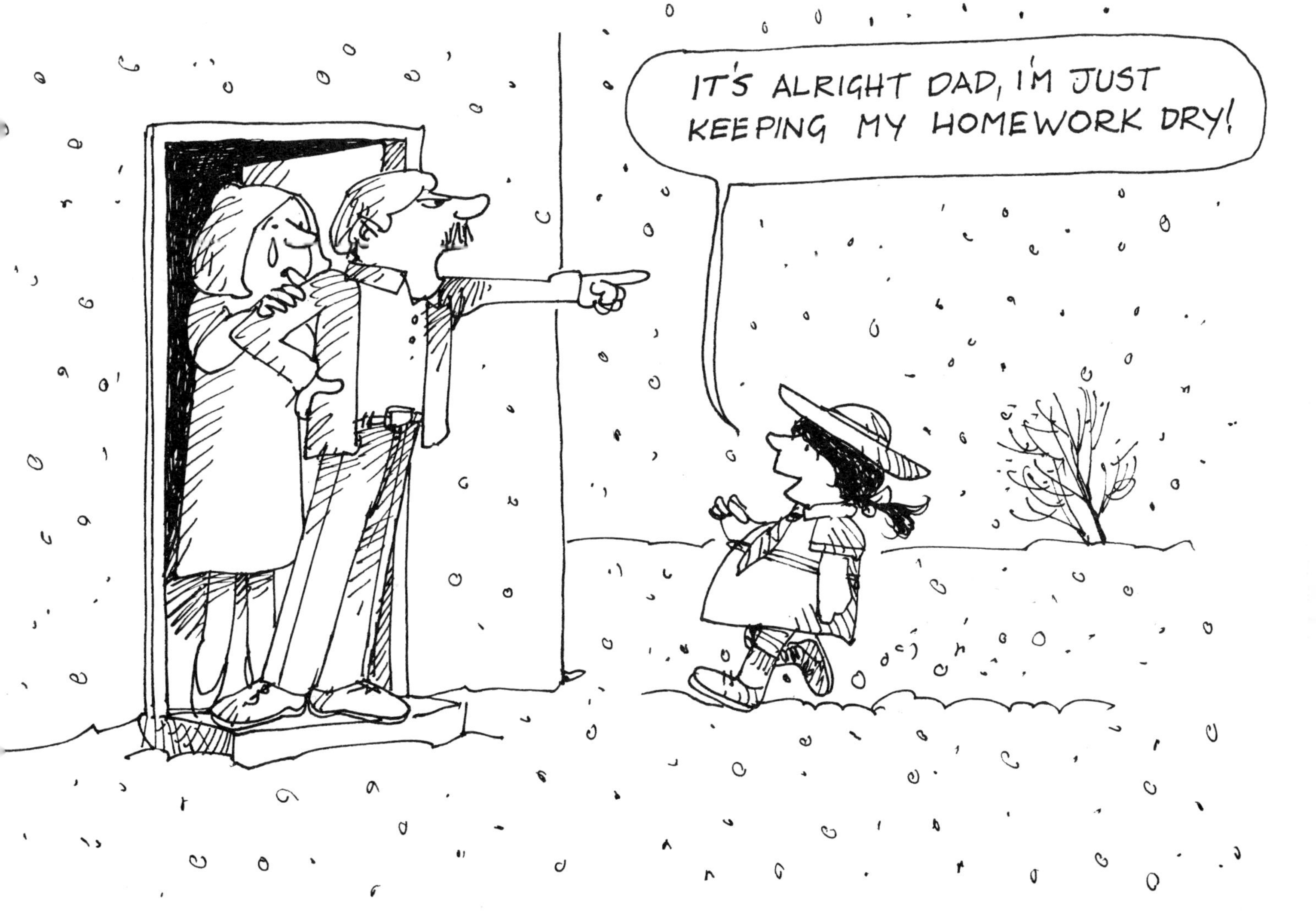
IT'S ALRIGHT DAD, I'M JUST KEEPING MY HOMEWORK DRY!

'NICE ARRANGEMENT DAD, YOU SHOULD TRY
FLOWERS NEXT...'

'DAD! STOP KIDDING AROUND, YOU DON'T STILL
HAVE SEX AT YOUR AGE?!'

'IT USED TO BE, 'NOT TILL THE KIDS ARE ASLEEP' NOW
IT'S 'HURRY, BEFORE THEY GET BACK FROM THE PUB!'

MORE! ANGELA **MORE!**...

'THERE'S A COINCIDENCE, NEITHER DOES MY WIFES
EXHUSBAND'S LOVERS GIRLFRIEND....'

'IT'S GOING TO TAKE ANOTHER TERM AT YOGA,
BEFORE WE CAN MANAGE Nº 23....'

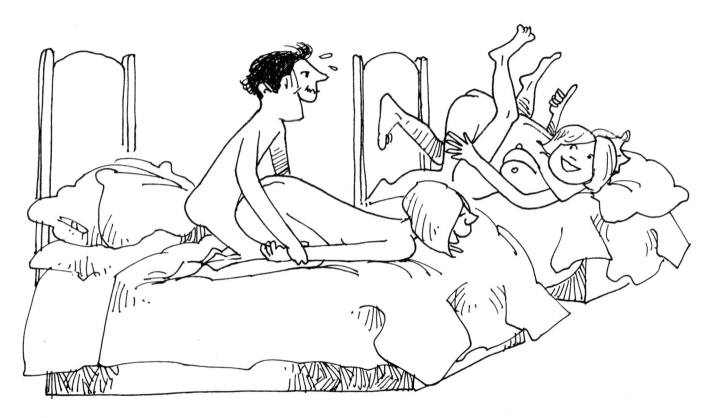

'YOUR IDEA OF GETTING TWIN BEDS IS WORKING
OUT RATHER WELL ELIZABETH...'

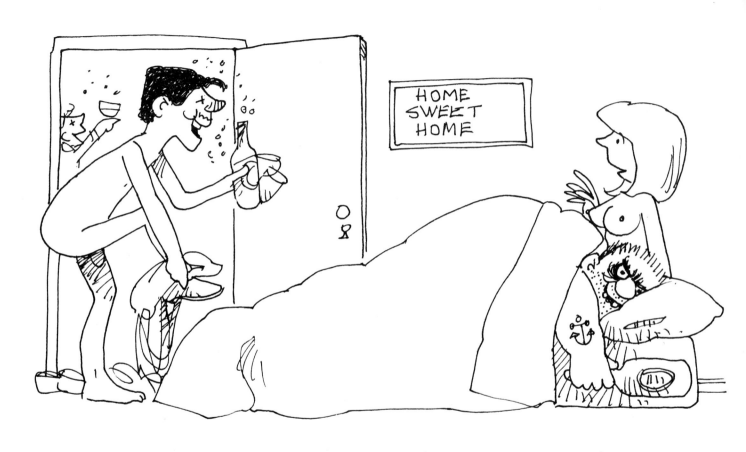

'GREAT PARTY, MRS O'LEARY, NOW LET'S YOU AND I GET DOWN TO SOME REAL PHYSICAL FUN AND GAMES...'

OH, HELLO DEAR, I DIDN'T KNOW YOU WERE INTERESTED IN PHOTOGRAPHY....?

' JOHN, I THINK THE ELECTRIC BLANKET IS STILL SWITCHED ON....'

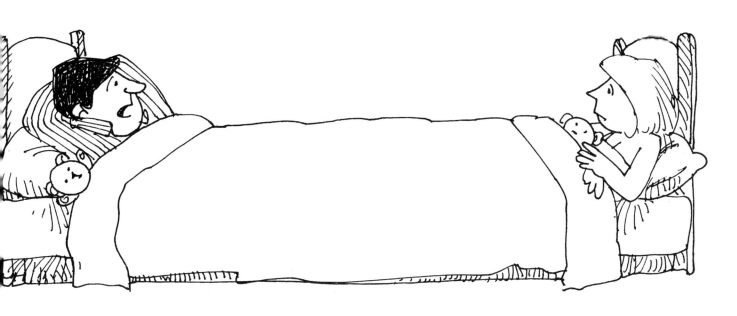

'WELL, HOW DO YOU THINK OUR TRIAL SEPARATION
IS WORKING OUT ?...'

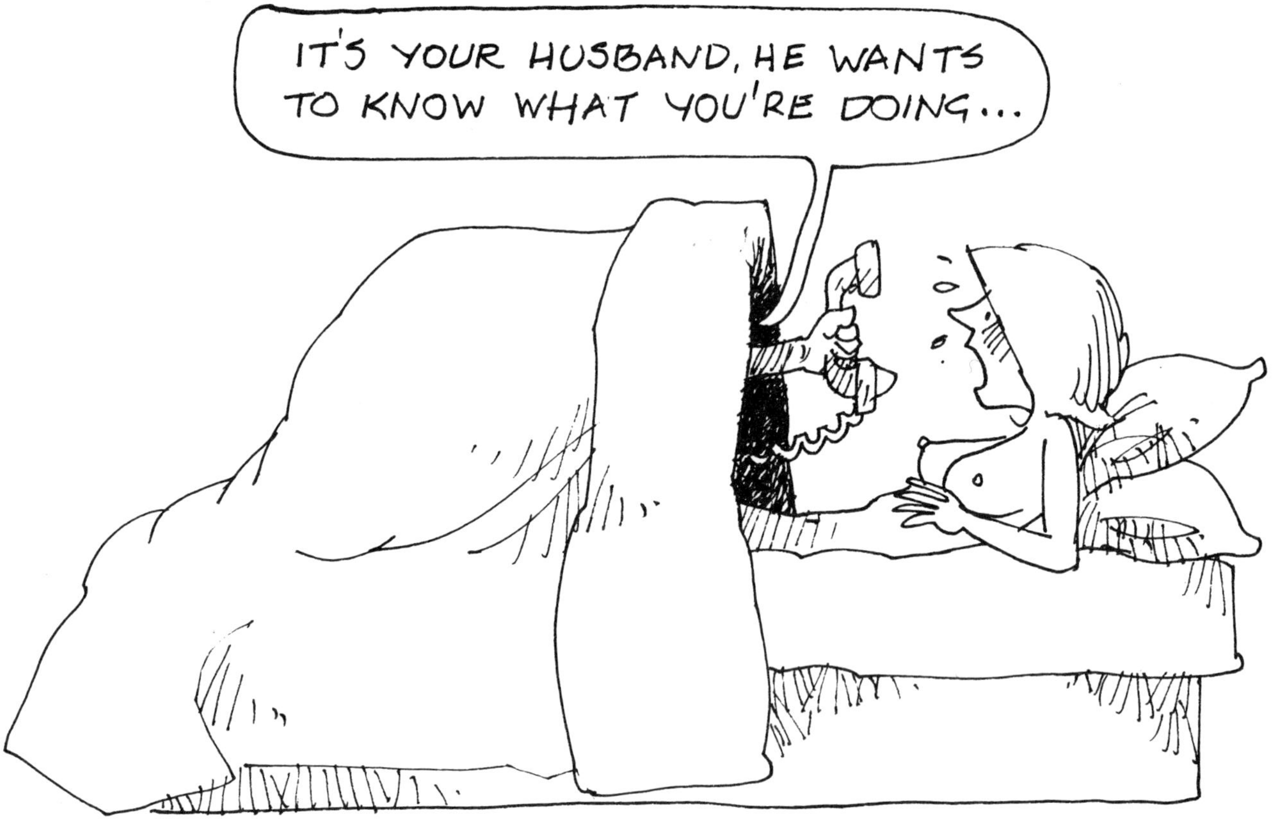
IT'S YOUR HUSBAND, HE WANTS TO KNOW WHAT YOU'RE DOING...

'YOU DIDN'T TELL ME YOU RAN A PLAY GROUP WHEN WE STARTED THIS AFFAIR!'

'YOU KNOW WHAT I MISS, ZELDA,? THE CHILDRENS LAUGHTER...'

"WELL, I'D LIKE TO RELIVE **MY** YOUTH IN A WARM HOTEL ROOM!"

'AH, I SEE WE'RE BACK TO THE SEXY CARDIGAN AGAIN...'

'ARE YOU GOING TO SLEEP, OR DO YOU WANT TO FOOL-AROUND...?'

'WOW! WHAT A GREAT PROGRAMME, NOW, WHAT WERE WE DOING?...'

'GROUP SEX IS SOMETHING ARTHUR AND I HAVE ALWAYS WANTED TO GET INTO ...'

'TRY AND GET INTO IT ALICE, YOU'RE SUPPOSED
TO BE A RECLINING NUDE!'

'I STILL GET THE URGE, BUT I CAN'T REMEMBER WHAT FOR ....'

'MY WIFE'S JUST LEFT ME!'

' WELL HELLO THERE, LONG TIME NO SEE.'...

'WE MET AT A WINE AND CHEESE-CAKE PARTY..'

'THERE MUST BE **ONE** WE COULD TRY...?'

'I HOPE I CAN REMEMBER HOW TO DO THIS....'

These are just some of the books in this series. Why not start a collection? If you can't find them contact us.

CAN SEX IMPROVE YOUR GOLF?
Do you get ball compression in the sweet spot? Do you keep losing your grip? What does fore-play have to do with golf? and can sex improve it? Don't 'play around' till you've read this book.

FARTING. All you want to know about 'blowing off' but were afraid to ask. The history of farting; the what, why, where and when of Farting; having fun with Farting and famous Farts including the 'silent-but-deadly' Fart. Don't miss this one.

IS THERE SEX AFTER 40? Now in a two book form. 'FOR HIM' and 'FOR HER'. Can one still get one's leg over at this great age? What do you do with the kids? Can you fit an affair in between shopping and the vet's? Why not get both books?

THE VERY, VERY, SEXY ADULT DOT-DOT BOOK. Draw your own very, very, sexy cartoon. That's if your hand isn't shaking too much Read the very, very, sexy caption your own cartoon, you'll need a mirror for this. While you've got th mirror, why don't you . . . .

ARE YOU STILL FLIRTY AT 30? Is there time for sex between collecting the kids and meeting your husband's train, and getting the film developed? Are you getting enough sexual harassment in the office? What you need is a nice sex cocktail.

ARE YOU FINISHED AT 50? Is it harder to get the old leg over these days? Harder to blow out your birthday candles? What about chasing your secretary around your desk? Do you need 5 minutes start? You're only finished when you're finished. Right?

THE NEW SEX DIET. How to lose weight everybody's favorite way. Sex causes friction. Friction causes burning. Burning causes calorie loss. Calorie loss means weight loss. So lose weight with lots and lots of SEX. The more you do it the more you lose. So get going.

HAPPY? BIRTHDAY. When you blow out the candles on your birthday cake --- is this a blow job Watch out for the birthday blackmail-o-gram . . . . . .
Anyway happy birthday bumping
Keep an eye open for the kids wit the video.

PENDULUM GALLERY PRESS   56 Ackender Road, Alton, Hampshire. GU34 1JS   Tel: (0420) 84483